Pussy Tie hits town

ILLUSTRATED BY GRAY JOLLIFFE

WORDS BY LAURIE GRAHAM

In my twenty years as a specialist I've never seen anything like this

A PAN ORIGINAL

PAN BOOKS

London, Sydney and Auckland

First published 1988 by Pan Books Ltd,
Cavaye Place, London SW10 9PG
9 8 7 6 5 4 3 2 1
Cartoons and Pussy Pie character © Gray Jolliffe 1988
Text © Laurie Graham 1988
ISBN 0 330 30269 8

Typesetting by Input Typesetting Ltd, London
Printed and bound in Spain by
Mateu Cromo Artes Graficas SA, Madrid

A Foreword

Did your mother warn you about floozies and hot tomatoes? Totty? Skirt? And golden-hearted whores? In spite of this does your world seem full of Nice Girls? Meet Pussy Pie, the tart who lurks within. Within, without, on top, thrice nightly. Make no mistake, this girl is a trooper. Mounted more often than Red Rum, nocturnal, diurnal, she never sleeps. Chastity belts, snow drifts, national frontiers, class wars, nothing stops her, *anno domini* – who cares! Pussy just gets on, and gets on with what she does best.

Still you've yet to meet her? Never mind. Every day somebody gets lucky.

In general, Pussy Pie lives somewhere between two extremes...

As every schoolboy knows, there are two kinds of girl. Those who will – as long as there's an R in the month, the dishes have been wiped, and you've put a ring on their finger – and those who just will.

What every schoolboy doesn't know, is that no matter what kind of a girl she is, she's not taxed by the question uppermost in a man's mind – Am I going to get laid tonight? Girls, even the ones who do, have other fish to fry. They have their own lives to run and other people's. Collars to starch, carpets to beat,

tomatoes to sculpt into waterlilies. The quality of life depends on a girl keeping her mind out of her knickers and firmly on the job in hand. Do you think flowers arrange themselves?

It is as well for humankind that one of the sexes can keep its head when all around are losing theirs. Without the steadying influence of women, the world population would have topped 20 billion, there would be a catastrophic shortage of caves, and no one would have invented Shake 'n'Vac. Through self-denial women have shaped the world. Would we know about the Bahamas if Mrs Columbus had made free with the bodily pleasures? Would Cabot have gone sail-about to Greenland if Mrs C. had been sitting on a warm welcome? Of course not. Behind any pioneering man there is a woman in control of her baser instincts. As Mavis Edison was often heard to say 'This won't get the light bulb invented.'

But the story doesn't end there. Sensible behaviour comes only slightly more naturally to women than it does to men. They just try harder. Somewhere in every girl, muffled by the folds of her apron, speaks the voice of moral turpitude. The voice of Pussy Pie. Sometimes she sleeps. But she never dies. Know the girl I mean?

The Pussy element

Received opinion has it that there are only two ways to excite a woman.

1. Open a charge account at Marks and Spencer.
2. Make Daz wash even whiter.

This just goes to show how little is understood about women. It totally ignores the Pussy Element. Wandering eyes, wandering hands, wandering minds. Do men truly believe they have cornered the entire Wandering Tendency? Is it really likely that the principal consumers of nylon pan scrubs and Day Time Television won't sometimes get the urge to let off the handbrake and roll? If the President of the United States of America can be on permanent standby for nookie, why not the woman who runs the wool shop? No reason at all. A girl can be going about her business, holding a pillowcase up to the light to see if it passes the window test, when the voice of wantonness calls her out to play. **'Beryl? This is Pussy speaking. The pillowcase looks terrific. Now let's go to the park and check the trouser situation.'**

It is a tribute to female self-control that the sheets ever get changed, and men can sit on park benches, free from fear.

"You simply have to realise that your fear of sex is totally irrational."

Unlike Man, whose rogue element lives almost exclusively down the front of his shorts, Pussy Pie also has a heart and a mind. This is her trouble. If one bit of her doesn't respond to a man, another bit does.

When a man looks at a woman he thinks, 'Will she? How soon? And does she have big tits?' Also, in these dangerous times 'Am I going to catch anything?' A woman's response is far more complex. 'How much does he make in a year? When did he last take a bath? Will he help me fix this roller blind?' Then Pussy chimes in. **'More to the point, will he woo me, flatter me, cherish me? Does he need mothering?**

Should I cook him dinner. Or be a good listener? Will he be rampant? Will he be hesitant? Will he take me with him, beyond the boundaries of self, into the maelstrom of ecstasy? And will it all last more than five minutes?'

Pussy is a girl who has known disappointment. But when she's down, does she stay down? Only if she likes it down there. Otherwise she comes back and back again. Hope is her middle name. *Somewhere* there has to be a man who knows about gallantry, chaste kisses and flowers.

The Trouser Snake speaks. 'Don't gimme that! Girls just wanna have fun! I heard it on Radio One.'

Pussy replies. **'Modern cynical trash!'**

The snake stands his ground. 'Well girls were made to love and kiss, I heard that on Radio Two.'

Pussy plays her shot from the base line. **'You got it Big Boy! Love *first*, kiss later. Listen to the lyrics, why don't you! Also, while we're on the subject, girls like it if you remember their name. Name remembering is a thing girls really go for. Stay awake *and* leave the phone off the hook, and you've got it made, Tiger!'**

Game, set and match to Miss Pie.

WHY MEN ARE AT THE MERCY OF WOMEN...

Men at risk

Men often ask 'Am *I* in any kind of danger from the Pussy pandemic?' This is not easy to answer. The scene changes constantly, and scientists are burning the midnight oil trying to solve this enduring mystery. All we can say at the present time is this, 'Provided you are of average build, have your own teeth, normal blood pressure, and the price of dinner for two, roughly speaking Yes, you are At Risk.'

But you don't have to take it lying down. There are many simple, inexpensive precautions you can take to reduce the danger to yourself. Self-help. That's the bottom line these days.

Show him your new tennis grip

Getting Pussy-wise

1. Avoid unlit, deserted Singles Bars.
2. Don't wear tight, provocative clothing.
3. If your job takes you unprotected into people's homes, be alert to anything unusual. Gas fitters are not normally required to do up zips, or help change the duvet cover.
4. Never accept lifts from women.
5. Talk your way out of trouble. Oblique remarks about penicillin will bring most situations under control.

Men who are least at risk are those who have
nothing obvious to offer a girl. Chartered
Accountants enjoy an excellent safety record,
second only to that of Certified Accountants.

This is cold comfort to the millions of men
who get made offers for their lengths of carpet,
pints of Gold Top, considered medical opinions,
or an extra half hour's use of their crevice tool.
But you've got to look at it this way: Trade is
what makes the world go round.

The Kitten _____

Before a girl takes even her first step or speaks her first word, Pussy's right there in the pram, offering advice. As she sensibly points out, there are two ways of getting what you want in life. Either you charm it out of people, or you get in the queue behind all those other honourable fools. Pussy puts her case in a manner that is very hard to resist.

'Smile at the Nice Man, Baby!
'Waaaaagh!'
'Just do as the pussy tells you. Smile at the Nice Man.'
'Waaa-waaaaa-waaaaaaagh!'
'Sometimes I wonder why I bother. Listen you stupid child! The Nice Man is your godfather. You are his *first* god-daughter. And in the pretty envelope there are Share Certificates. Beechams stock! Now smile!'
'Ga-ga.'
'She did it! I knew she would.'

Once she's out of her pram, Pussy can really get to work on a girl.

'Today I am three. The sun is shining and everyone thinks I'm cute, sing tra-la. What shall I do? I could bath my doll. I could ride on my tricycle. I could paint a picture of An House, I could skip. I could jump . . . I know! I'll invite the boys round and hang upside down on my climbing frame! I wonder how much I should charge?'

'The girl is learning.'

But some little girls never learn. They can't because they were born with a thing called integrity. Show them any deal and straight way they start looking for ways to clean it up. It's a shame. But then, it's not every girl that looks good in diamonds anyway.

When Pussy is up and running there's not a lot that will divert her. A dirty oven possibly, but certainly not *anno domini*. Age does not wither her. Well it does, but it doesn't stop her. This is the lousy paradox she must live with. When she is young she has a bloom on her cheek, an energy of purpose, buoyancy of the buoyant parts, and *no technique whatsoever*. By the time she has technique she also has wrinkles, varicose veins, and serious structural movement in her foundations. She has confidence too, and confidence can be *very* sexy, but not if it needs hiding under heavy-duty polythene. She has become a National Monument. A Listed Ruin. Held in affectionate regard. A legend in her own time, respected for her great antiquity. Where's the fun in that?

This girl wants to do some serious frolicking.
Did she ask you to escort her across the road?
Did she? Are you sure she didn't offer you
Tango lessons? And didn't you think 'If we tango
tonight, tomorrow she may want to play Hide
the Wienie!'

Own up! Didn't you think 'Who could do that
with something that belongs in the British
Museum!'

Life can be a bitch at times.

The spare rib?

For many years a story has been doing the rounds about Adam, a spare rib, and the Man Upstairs, and another, concerning a snake, an apple and a fig-leaf jockstrap. No mention, you may have noticed, of Pussy Pie. But she was there. Right there. Time now to set the record straight.

First off the production line was Eve. And she wasn't made from anyone else's spare parts. There may have been a rib or two knocking about, spilled maybe from an old take-away bag, but no one was using them to create women.

Eve was a nice girl. Clean living, honest, kind to animals. The Big Cheese, Ruler of All, was well pleased with what he had wrought. Then, who should roll in but the Queen of Slut City and *she* wasn't a Garden of Eden kind of person at all. This girl wanted fun. She wanted to set the joint jumping. She needed the companionship of someone livelier, and less serious minded than the diligent Eve. Someone with bigger muscles, for the hewing of wood and the drawing of water, and some basic equipment for games of Hide the Sausage on long winter evenings, because the snake had told her 'Positively *never* again'.

So she asked the Man Upstairs. He'd got rather a lot on, and when he came up with Adam it was a case of take it or leave it. A bit

of a rush job, but still. . . . When Eve saw what fun it all was *she* wanted a little go. And as Pussy pointed out, **'I have seen the future, and it'll do. Also, it's willing to hunt for supper. Which sure beats the hell out of a moth-eaten snake!'** The rest is just a load of theology.

Great Pussies of yesteryear_

History has never walked a straight path. Its twists and turns and sidetracks are what make it so engrossing a subject to its students. Is it all predestined? Or merely a series of random collisions, whose consequences are impossible to predict? I dunno.

What is certain is that the influence of Puss-ism in history has been largely overlooked.

It is generally agreed by scholars that it was the humble stirrup that won the Battle of Hastings for Willie the Conk. We hear nothing

I never yield to the temptation of denying myself a seeing-to

of the role of Edith Hot Lips Swanstrangler, Bit on the Side to the Bedchamber of King Harold. At last the truth may be told.

October, 1066; Friday the thirteenth. Harold knew he should get up. Ede wasn't going to stop him. But the voice of depravity spoke. **'It's only seven. Them Norms won't even be cleared up from breakfast. C'mon Hal! One more for the road?'** In this casual manner England was given away to the French.

And the Puss has done worse than hinder great men. She has been her own worst enemy. How many physicists know that the Laws of Motion were first proposed by Gloria Good Time Dunnitt in 1683? She was just so busy clocking the butcher's boy, she forgot to write it down. Next thing she knew, Isaac Newton was picking up the bouquets.

Saddest of all, how many people know Shakespeare had a sister? She'd just dipped her quill and written 'Hung be the heavens with black, yield day to night!' when Slut City beckoned.

'Writers need to do research' whispered Pussy Pie. **'Let's go out and see if it's true what they say about men with big feet.'**

Weeks later young Will found the abandoned page.

'What's this then Connie?' he enquired.

'Oh just Henry VI, Part I' she replied. 'Fill a bit in for me if you like.'

Good sports

Women are normally full of good sense. They recognize from a very early age that there is nothing natural about sport. OK, running is natural. It dates from the days when ravening wolves and great hairy beasts pursued mankind up hill and down dale, and running was a pretty smart thing to do. But ball games? Just a silly method of letting off steam. Only men would entertain such foolishness. Women let off their

steam scrubbing at nasty stains.

But there are women who never miss a match. How can this be? What makes women endure the wind and the rain and the queue at the turnstile for the sight of men and balls? The answer is in the question. It is the sight of the men they go for. The shoulders, the thighs, the curve of the butt. A tangle of bodies caked with mud, sweat and tears, as phlegm and rude words fly through the air and muscle and sinew are pitted against the might of the referee's pencil. Men and balls, balls and men.

No prizes for guessing the name of the girl hanging round the changing-room door. A fine example of the Pussy Factor at work. Again.

The lone voice of Pussy is easy to ignore. She's no contest for all those other voices competing for the attention of a normal woman.

'Load the washer.' 'No, don't load the washer. Bake the pie, clean the windows, *then* load the washer.' 'What's all this with pies?' 'Can we please have a little action in the dog-walking department?' 'Dogs we can live without, clean shirts we can't. Like I said, load the washer. Then call your mother!' In the midst of this Tower of Babel she's never going to hear one small voice whispering **'Let's go out someplace and interfere with men.'** *Unless* it is presented as a choral work for massed voices. Get enough Pussies singing the old siren song in unison and before you know it you have a Girls' Night Out. Then, when three or more are gathered together, with a bottle of Asti inside them, let all cautious men beware.

When Pussy is on the prowl, eager for a good time, men's bodies become mere playthings. And if she should start to sober up, if she should start to realize that she's raising the portcullis for a travelling salesman from Walsall whose personal chemistry scores

approximately zilch on the Scale of Interesting Trouser, her sisters will be quick to top up her glass and egg her on.

'He's crazy for you, Vera!'

'But he's wearing a toupee!'

'Hair loss is a sign of virility.'

'I hate men who wear pinkie rings!'

'But he has a car. A nice car with no oily rags in the back. He also has a hotel room, a fat roll of twenties in his pocket, and he travels in silk underwear. We could be talking free samples all round!'

'**OK. I'll overlook the toupee, the ring, the nylon socks that are the colour of cat shit, and the wall-eye. What sizes shall I get?**

Vera buys this deal because she is outnumbered. The will of the Pussy Pack is impossible to resist.

There are a few virtuous maidens who are reckoned never to have been visited by that Great Pussy in the Brain. WRAC Colonels, schoolmistresses in brogues, librarians.

This is all very hard to believe. Are they seriously telling us that the sauce-pot who has wheedled her way into No. 10 Downing Street, still hasn't surfaced in the Officers' Mess? This can't be true! She only has to cut a hole in the fence. Perhaps she is there, but cunningly disguised. Her loose intentions targeted on a rather different kettle of khaki.

'Cor! Get an eyeful of that.'

'Desist, you filthy little pervert, or I'll have you cashiered!'

'All right! No need to be so touchy! I was only remarking how nicely turned out the Sergeant was.'

And libraries? She must have heard of libraries. The darkest recesses of the Reserve Stack would be a perfect hiding-place for the Demon Harlot.

'Psst! Olive! Come in here a minute!'

'Out of the question. I have to dust Social Anthropology.'

'Go on! Just for a minute? Come and dust Oriental Erotica.'

'Admission to Erotica and Scatology is limited strictly to the Chief Librarian.'

'But no one's looking.'

'Mr Snetterton might be.'

'True.'

'He might catch me in the act. He might put me over his knee and punish me severely.'

'At last! I knew you'd start to see things my way.'

Tart Deco

Any working girl will tell you that the easiest thing to wear when you have to make three trips to the Laundromat, change a light bulb, and roast a chicken, is something sensible. Like a tweed skirt, a cable stitch cardigan, a pair of sneakers and a tea cosy hat. And underneath? A panty girdle, Sombrero Tan tights, and a grubby shoulderstrap, fetchingly secured by a safety pin. Comfort, you see, is pretty well everything. But not for old Pussy Pants. Practicalities don't concern her because she doesn't do a whole lot. When you lie around all day eating chocolates and undermining the Puritan Ethic, any old négligé will do.

So what is her recipe for sexcessful dressing?' **'Drape and slit, darling! Drape and slit!'**

This is the little devil that leads a girl to the silk knicker counter when actually she should be shopping for Odor-Eaters. She's the reason girls buy heels they can't walk in.

'Come and look at the pretty shoes.'

'Silence! My shopping list says Moon Boots.'

'But *these* are pretty. *These* have mirrored heels.
and the suede is *very* soft.'

'No good in the snow.'

'In these you'll never need to go out in the snow.
In these, men will queue to go out in the snow
for you!'

'Too high to walk in.'

'**Who's walking?**'

'OK. We'll buy the pretty shoes. Now be quiet.
I have to get a windproof jacket.'

'**Why bother? Do as I do. Just wear a fur coat.
And underneath, nothing at all!**'

'That must save a lot of laundry.'

'**You know, I could really make something of
this girl.**'

Shaping up

It's hard to stay out of the gym these days. Everyone's taking care of themselves. Lycra leotards are now available in sizes 20 to 28 and rising, floors have been reinforced, and it's getting easier to buy herbal tea bags than it is to find someone who'll fill you a bagel with smoked salmon and cream cheese.

Even that indolent creature The Puss, has taken stock. She has accepted that this is the Age of the Body Beautiful, so if you're hoping to Put Out, stands to reason you gotta Work Out.

Always a girl to spot a short cut, she has devised a ten-minute route that will exercise her three most important assets.

1. A thorough warm-up is vital, and with a partner it's a lot more fun. Go steady though. This is no time to pull a muscle.

2. Now get out of bed.

3. The Women's Movement. Mainly this involves the pelvis. First lie flat on your back, and imagine Mel Gibson nailed to the ceiling. Try to reach him. Not with a turntable ladder, you ditz! Go on, you can do it. With your *pelvis*. Raise those hips and shout 'Hang on Mel, help is on the way!' Then lower, and repeat.

4. The Nutcracker. For this you *must* wear fishnets and suspenders. Lean against a wall. The bathroom wall will do. You'll get faster results leaning against a wall in Wardour Street, but you'll also need a good brief to get you bailed.

Now, let your coat fall open, wet your lips, bend one knee and *brace* your supporting leg. Change legs and repeat. Keep going until someone makes you an offer, or your fishnets start to bag around the knee.

5. The Tongue Twister. The tongue is the most neglected muscle in the body. And this is where the Pussy Pie Workout has the edge on Jane Fonda. All it takes is five verses of *The Rime of the Ancient Mariner* daily, with a lump of treacle toffee in your mouth. And you'll be so glad you bothered. Like the girl says, **'Good sex takes a lot of licking'.**

These are cut-throat times for anyone trying to earn a crust. Achievers are getting younger and more ruthless. *The* colour this season is barracuda grey, and scalps are being worn around the neck. You have to rise early, and fight dirty, and girls are not excused. The number of Men Only bastions still to be stormed can now be counted on the fingers of one hand, and girls know that if they want it, they can have it. They just have to sharpen up and Go For It.

Here is a 5-point plan that will improve a girl's chances of career success.

1. Know your onions.
2. Make sure someone very influential, big-hearted and secure knows you know your onions.
3. Be assertive.
4. Don't wear cheap polyester.
5. Never weep.

Then there is the Other Method. The one favoured by that idle little minx in the satin knickers. The Pussy Plan.

1. Be sure you know the size of everyone else's onions.
2. Only adjust your stockings in front of a very big onion indeed.
3. Dress to complement the casting couch.
4. Always defer to authority, seniority, and the long arm of the boardroom round your waist.
5. Check your lipstick.

See what the Equal Opportunities Commission is up against? The advantage of the Pussy Plan for Career Advancement is that it can produce very fast results. In fact, if the Chairman's wife has been keeping him on short rations, a clever girl can enjoy a meteoric rise, *almost* to the top. The feminist position on this ploy is that Pussy should be taken to a vet and seen to.

Men used to ask girls out to dinner. Nice Girls treated these invitations with caution, although that little voice was always there, purring **'Sure you're free for dinner! Tell the man you're also free for coffee at his place, liqueurs, and Matters Arising.'**

Then Big Business begat the Expense Account, and the Expense Account begat The Working Lunch, and there was much rejoicing. Men used the Working Lunch to woo small Japanese accountants. Sometimes they used it to woo secretaries with large breasts. And as the tide of feminism rose, Successful Women used it to flummox Head Waiters.

Lunch is a far more complicated transaction than dinner. It may be the scene of some hard bargaining, clear headed, over a bottle of designer water. Or it may be intimate. It can lead to A Lost Afternoon. Realizing this, The Nice Girl has enough sense to avoid knee contact, and eat nothing more lavish than an *omelette aux fines herbes.* Indebtedness can lead to all kinds of trouble. Mainly horizontal.

The Successful Woman knows this too. The only thing on her mind is 'Can I close this deal, dump this nerd, and make the next flight to Kennedy?' But here comes the difficulty that women, who are comparative newcomers to the lunch scene, find themselves in. That damned Pussy always turns up.

'Don't be a spoilsport, Audrey!' she whispers. **'Order some of the bubbly stuff. Show the gentleman a good time!'**

'Who let you in? Clear off! I've ordered a half of the Merlot, and I'm here to get his signature on this contract.'

'Doesn't he have cute ears?'

'I have another meeting at three.'

'Audrey, take some advice? Many men can't sign a contract from a cold start. Slip off your shoe and give him a little surprise under the tablecloth!'

'He signed!'

'Of course he signed! Still mad at me for showing?'

So what's this Emancipation thing anyway?

The last twenty years have brought conflict between the sexes, the like of which has never been seen before. To paraphrase – Men want girls to carry on wiggling their bottoms, and girls want men to shut up, grow up, and hand over the car keys.

It began in the early Seventies, when women had their consciousnesses raised. They looked out and behold, they saw that verily, Man was a jerk. Then a bright spark from a Think Tank suggested raising men's consciousnesses.

Trolley jacks and block and tackle were sent for. Armies of women heaved and toiled, for little personal gain. And lo, slowly the male consciousness was raised. Just a bit.

But men didn't like it up there. They felt strangely nauseous. They asked to be lowered at once, and women, or Wimmin, as they had become, were most annoyed.

But feminism didn't falter because of a few whingeing men. A third party was involved. A turn-coat, a sneaking, pandering go-between who has always held the balance of power between men and women. Pussy Pie, the girl who put a torch to the Women's Charter.

'Sisters of Lysistrata, lay down your dusters, trample your corsets underfoot! March with us, to reclaim the night!'

'Girls, girls! Hold the marching! Listen to Pussykin a minute. Have I got this right? You want these men sorted once and for all? You want them put in their place? No problem. That's exactly where they want to be. No need to get ugly with the Doc Marten boots! Tell me, did you ever try taking a pair of silk stockings and tying a man to the. . . .'